MW00791170

We do not stop playing because we grow old; we grow old because we stop playing.

—Anonymous

Innovative Roping presents...

Jumping Rope the Second Time Around

Carlos Coffman

CCG

Coffman Consultants Group
P.O. Box 2136 • Bowie, Maryland 20718
www.irope@prodigy.net

Carlos Coffman

Library of Congress Cataloging-in-Publication Number:
98-094927
ISBN: 0-9665897-0-X
First Edition (c) 1998
Copyright (c) 1998 Carlos Coffman
All Rights Reserved

No portion of this book may be reproduced by any process without written permission of Coffman Consultants Group at P.O.Box 2136, Bowie, Maryland 20718-2136.

vi

ATTENTION: CORPORATIONS AND SCHOOLS

JUMPING ROPE THE SECOND TIME AROUND is available at quantity discounts with bulk purchases for educational, business, or sales promotional use. For information please write CCG Special Sales, P.O Box 2136, Bowie, Maryland 20718-2136. Please supply title of book, ISBN number, quantity (10 or more), how the book will be used, and date needed.

DISCLAIMER:

All information contained in this book is for educational purposes only and the reader assumes the risk for the use of this information. Before commencing any health, fitness or sports training program, please consult your physician or health care professional. The author assumes no responsibility for any adverse consequences resulting from the use of the information in this book.

IROPE and the Victory logo ( ) are registered trademarks of Innovative Roping/IROPE, Inc.

Photography by Bobie Capel

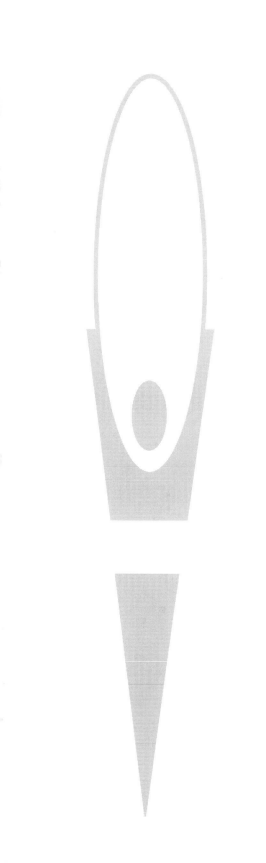

Carlos Coffman

This book is dedicated to the memory of my grandmother, Mrs. Jenetha Verona Facey, and to my parents Grant and Hazel Coffman and brothers Grant and Samuel for their never ending love and guidance.

Dedico este libro a la memoria de mi querida abuela, Señora Jenetha Verona Facey y a mis padres Grant y Hazel Coffman y a mis hermanos Grant y Samuel por su constante amor y dedicación a mis esfuerzos.

vii

Carlos Coffman

IROPE...in motion

Table of Contents

Carlos Coffman

Man's mind, once stretched by a new idea, never returns to its original dimensions.
- Oliver Wendell Holmes

Acknowledgments:

Jumping Rope the Second Time Around, is the product of what started out as a newsletter to inform friends and the curious about this "new twirl in fitness." Although several years of "rope-walking" road races throughout the country drew an overwhelming degree of interest among many, only a few could actually experience first hand the many benefits associated with this style of "jump roping." As the newsletter went through several revisions and as more people began to tell me how Innovative Roping (IROPING, for short) helped put physical activity back into their daily lives, the idea of *Jumping Rope the Second Time Around* was born.

First and foremost I thank God for giving me the inspiration and opportunity to share this program with you and giving me the family, friends and critics whose time and effort went into putting this book together. I would like to send a special thanks to Community Clinic, Inc. in Rockville, Maryland for including the IROPE program in their community outreach programs.

I also thank the photographer, Bobie Capel and the models, Terry Landicho and Doug Kutchman for their dedication and enthusiasm. My thanks also go to Kevin Levrone for the use of World Gym in Severna Park, Maryland.

Because jumping rope is so closely tied to rhythm and rhythm to music, I can't help but thank the many musicians whose music has inspired me and whose tunes, melodies and compositions run through my mind as I workout. Among them are Kirk Whalum, Tim Curry, Kyle Turner, Regina Carter, and the musical geniuses of Miles Davis, Dizzy Gillespie, John Coltrane, Bob Marley, Mongo Santamaria, Antonio Carlos Jobim, and Mahalia Jackson. Also, my sincere thanks go to all who have been willing to learn the

Carlos Coffman

Innovative Roping techniques and apply them to their workout regimens and especially to those who have offered words of encouragement and inspiration during the races.

——*Carlos*——

You cannot discover new oceans unless you have the courage to lose sight of the shore. —unknown

Carlos Coffman

PREFACE

Dear Reader:

If you have the desire to improve your health through physical activity but do not know where to start or are confused about how to choose between the latest fitness crazes, fads, "must have" state-of-the-art exercise equipment and exclusive health club memberships, then *Jumping Rope the Second Time Around* is for you. Because breakthroughs in fitness equipment are introduced to the public every year, more and more people, especially those of us striving for a healthier life style, find ourselves asking; "Which piece of equipment is right for me?" By trial and error, we sometimes find that perfect match. But, too often that match is not made until we have spent a good deal of money, time, and sometimes even suffered minor injuries in the process. And what do you have to show for it? Well, if you're like me, a basement, closet, or garage full of gadgets and equipment whose only function is to collect dust.

xv

Close your eyes and think about one of the first pieces of exercise equipment you were introduced to, even before your first bicycle. Do you remember what it was? Well, most likely it was probably a jump rope. Remember the fun, the games, the rhymes? Jumping rope was so much fun that it wasn't even thought of as exercise. That "childhood toy" can once again be the answer to your fitness needs.

Jumping Rope the Second Time Around offers something totally different than what's been offered by other fitness books and videos. In fact, it's been described as a radical and revolutionary way of using the jump rope to condition the entire body without tricks, gimmicks and additional state-of-the-art equipment.

What's so different about **IROPING**? The twirl. As you will see, today's fitness experts are still teaching jump roping the same way it has always been taught. "Twirl the rope with your wrists using a forward twirling motion," they say. Unfortunately not even the experts with the latest information on exercise physiology, biomechanics, and other scientific data have bothered to investigate a more efficient and effective use of the jump rope for total body conditioning. In other words, because nothing has changed in the world of jump roping, until now, you've been missing the extraordinary fitness that jump roping can provide!

Today's experts often teach jump roping to an older audience the same way they would teach 10 year old children. If you can recall the last time you picked up a jump rope as an adult, you probably put it down as quickly as you picked it up. The major reason for this is that you tried using the same jump roping technique you learned as a child with the body of an adult. As you get older your body goes through changes that don't permit you to do the things you once could when you were much younger. So, today you must be selective of the types of physical and recreational activities in which you participate.

xvi

I've written *Jumping Rope the Second Time Around,* to introduce you to the most efficient and effective way to use the jump rope as a way to condition your entire body without having to spend a lot of money. This book will guide you and help you establish the foundation for your own personal jump rope fitness program. Whether you are just becoming reacquainted with fitness, looking to make a change in your fitness routine, or a frequent traveler in need of an alternative exercise program while on the road, *Jumping Rope the Second Time Around* can help you meet your daily physical activity needs and reach your fitness goals.

Jumping rope is one of the few exercise activities that can be done just about anywhere and at anytime. With that in mind, this companion guide was purposefully made short and simple for easy portability on business trips, vacations and even trips to the gym. Photographs of various techniques from measuring the rope to actual exercises should be used as references as well as the sections on setting goals and charting your progress.

This book contains photographs of various jump roping techniques, actual exercises, some of my favorite motivational quotes, and a section on setting goals with removable copies of progress charts. These tools will help you establish a safe and sound jump roping program and will help you achieve your fitness goals and expectations.

With patience and practice you will soon experience the benefits of **IROPE**.

I - Improve Flexibility
R - Reduce Stress
O - Overcome Boredom
P - Promote a Healthy Self Image
E - Enjoy Life!

Stay Healthy,

Carlos Coffman, President
Innovative Roping, Inc.

What is skillfully established will not be uprooted; what is skillfully grasped will not slip away. Thus it is honored for generations.

- Tao Te Ching

INTRODUCTION

There is nothing, I think, more unfortunate than to have soft, chubby, fat-looking children who go to watch their school play basketball every Saturday and regard that as their week's exercise.
- John F. Kennedy, Address at U.S. Children's Bureau, Washington, D.C., April 9, 1962.

In today's fast paced, high stressed society, only a small percentage of the United States population is involved in routine fitness activity, whether it's a pick-up game of basketball or tennis, a daily swim, walk, jog or, weekly visits to the local health club. The 1996 US Surgeon General's Report on Physical Activity and Health, concluded that approximately 15 percent of US adults engage regularly (three times a week for at least 20 minutes) in vigorous activity during leisure time." A more recent report from the Centers for Disease Control and Prevention released in late 1998 found that physical inactivity plagues not only urban areas but also rural areas and the South. The lack of physical activity in the form of exercise continues to have a tremendous impact on health care costs, our individual health, and the health of our family members, loved ones, friends, neighbors and co-workers. This was re-affirmed by Donna E. Shalala, former Secretary of the Department of Health and Human Services, in the same report where she stated "…our nation needs to become more physically active to reduce the needless morbidity and mortality associated with physically inactive lifestyles."

The Surgeon General's report does not stop with the inactivity of the adult population, but also points out an even more alarming concern and fact that, today's youth may not be getting the proper amount of daily exercise needed for optimum health, and that "participation in all types of physical activity declines strikingly as age or grade in school increases."   This is frightening because today's physically inactive youth will become tomorrow's physically inactive parents, teachers and leaders unless we reverse this trend.

Think back to when you were much younger. If you were like most children, at some time in your life you probably owned a jump rope or at least played jump rope games with your peers. Jumping rope is really one of those activities that we all have had some experience with. Whether you recall taking your first rope straight out of a box or making your own with a clothesline, a piece of rope found in the garage, or even an old extension cord, you had hours of fun creating rhymes or imitating the fancy footwork and speed of the likes of the Mohammed Ali's, Joe Frazier's, Sugar Ray Leonard's, or Roberto Duran's of the day.

Back then you didn't even realize that by jumping rope you were physically conditioning your body and improving your coordination skills that would be transferable to the basketball, volleyball and tennis courts, football and soccer fields, the dance floor, and even sports like track and field and gymnastics.

Even if you believe the excuses that jumping rope is still kids' play, you're too old, it's bad on the knees, or it requires a lot of coordination, this book will demonstrate that jumping rope can be done by just about anyone at anytime in their lives. Unlike the traditional forward twirling of the rope, Innovative Roping employs solely the backward twirling motion. Why? First, the backward twirling motion is less stressful on the body. The upper body automatically assumes a naturally relaxed posture by positioning the upper body weight **behind** the knees as opposed to **over** the knees when twirling forward. This virtually eliminates the harsh impact of the jump on the ankles, knees and lower back. Second, the backward twirling motion allows the jumper to move in different directions and simulate various sport specific movements as opposed to primarily jumping in place which can become boring. Finally, twirling the rope backwards allows the jumper to safely condition all major muscle groups of the body.

I designed this program to be fun, challenging, and most of all, safe for just about everyone, including:

- people over 25 years of age;
- busy parents;
- professionals whose extremely busy schedules prohibit regular daily visits to the gym; and
- people seeking to improve or maintain their physical and mental health.

Using the Innovative Roping program will add a new, liberating dimension to how you look at and incorporate fitness in your daily life.

BENEFITS OF JUMP ROPING / IROPING

There are several benefits associated with traditional jump roping, both as an individual exercise and as a sport. These include: cardiorespiratory conditioning; improved hand-eye-foot coordination, agility and flexibility; freedom to create new steps; portability; and low cost.

Once you have learned the backward twirling technique and multidirectional movement (the ability to move through the arc of the twirling rope), a totally new dimension of fitness benefits become apparent. What are they? and Why are they so unique to IROPING?

Starting with the backward twirl, upper body muscle conditioning has never been made so easy. By twirling the rope backwards, the arm and chest muscles are used more effectively than when wrist action is used in the forward twirl. Because the rope is being twirled in a backward motion, movements such as rowing and biceps curls can be simulated as effectively as if one were using a rowing machine and weights. Using this technique allows you to focus on certain muscle groups during your workout without having to stop jumping to move to another piece of equipment.

5

Also the upper body weight automatically assumes a more neutral relaxed position behind the knees, eliminating the need to jump higher and at a more rapid rate in order to clear the rope beneath the feet. This allows you to achieve a greater level of balance and allows more impact distribution throughout the legs. Therefore, the backward twirl drastically minimizes the amount of impact to the ankles, knees, and lower back, making it a truly low impact exercise suitable for almost anyone!

Additional fitness benefits unique to **IROPING** become apparent when multidirectional movement is incorporated while moving through the arc of the twirling rope. Because multidirectional movement is added to the workout, more lower body muscle groups are exercised. The benefits include toning the calves, quadriceps, and gluteal muscles. Now you can cast away your fears of having over developed muscles that would be disproportionate to the rest of your body after prolonged roping. Furthermore, by adding multi-directional movement, you are able to benefit from practicing and executing various footwork drills closely resembling tennis, track, basketball, volleyball, and other sport specific movements, thereby increasing speed, agility, coordination, and endurance. This is what really makes **IROPING** the ultimate cross-training exercise.

YOUR SAFETY ALWAYS COMES FIRST

If you are 25 years of age or older this program was designed especially for you. Let's start by reviewing a few safety tips that will get you to a smooth, trouble-free start.

- Before you begin any new exercise program you should undergo a physician-supervised exercise stress test or medical checkup to determine your fitness level and any restrictions that should be followed.

- Warm up before you begin your actual exercise drills and gradually decrease the intensity of the drills as you taper off your workout. Warming up first and cooling down last are two very important elements to any exercise routine that help prevent injury and unnecessary muscle soreness.

- If you experience any pain while exercising, **STOP AT ONCE**. Consult your physician before continuing or commencing any other exercise program.

- While exercising, wear comfortable athletic clothing and cross-trainers or aerobic shoes that provide support and comfort.

- Drink plenty of water throughout the course of the day as well as prior to, during and following exercise.

- Remember to be patient, stay relaxed and focused.

- Listen to your body and have fun.

A journey of a thousand miles must begin with a single step.
- Chinese Proverb

GETTING STARTED: THE BASICS

Choosing a quality rope. Whether you are an experienced jump roper or just getting started, choosing the right rope can be a bit confusing at first. The most common ropes that you may be familiar with are the plastic beaded, leather (usually the first choice for boxers) and thin vinyl ropes primarily used for speed workouts and tricks. There are also the slower ropes that may come in the form of cotton (similar to a clothesline) and the weighted or heavy ropes which may or may not have weighted handles. Most of the ropes mentioned here are either too fast or too slow to successfully accomplish many of the **Innovative Roping** techniques.

The best type of rope for **IROPING** that can be purchased from your local sporting goods store should have an adjustable length rubber cord approximately 1/4" in diameter, comfortable handles, and a smooth twirling motion. If you prefer a rope with weighted handles, make sure the weights are removable.

Measuring the rope.

figure 1

To determine if a rope is the proper size or length, hold the handles in your hands and cross your arms slightly above the bottom of your rib cage; the arc of the rope should rest on the ground (see figure 1). If the arc of the rope is off of the ground, or resting on the tops of your shoes, the rope is too short and will cause you to jump too high. If more than the arc of

9

the rope is resting on the ground, the rope is too long and you will be forced to alter the correct arm position needed to twirl the rope smoothly or shorten the rope by wrapping the excess around the wrist. In either case, if the rope is not adjustable do not make the purchase. *Remember, jumping too high or improperly can result in injury.*

Notes:

_____
_____
_____
_____
_____
_____
_____
_____
_____
_____
_____
_____
_____
_____
_____
_____
_____
_____
_____
_____
_____
_____
_____
_____
_____
_____
_____
_____

11

If the ax is dull, and one does not sharpen the edge, then he must use more strength; but wisdom brings success.
The Holy Bible - Ecclesiastes 10:10

INNOVATIVE ROPING TECHNIQUE TIPS

A NOTE ON TWIRLING: Innovative Roping uses a backward twirling of the rope primarily to reduce impact and stress on the ankles, knees and lower back.

The jump rope techniques described in this manual may be new to you and seem awkward at first. However, perform the exercises very carefully and slowly, first without the rope and then with the rope. Concentrate on form not speed.

To begin: hold the handles between your index and middle fingers (see figure 2). This position will prevent you from squeezing the handles which contributes to premature arm, shoulder, and neck muscle fatigue common in traditional stationary jumping. After you've practiced this technique and have become accustomed to not squeezing the handles, you can hold the handles in a more traditional manner. By twirling in a natural backward motion, your hands actually become cradles for the jump rope handles, there by eliminating the need for squeezing.

13

figure 2

- With the rope beginning at the front of your feet, begin twirling by positioning your elbows close to your waist and your forearms at about 45 degree angles from your waist (see figure 3). Slowly move your arms in an upward and circular motion. You may want to try this first without the rope just to develop a feel for the movement. One way to obtain proper arm positioning is to hold the ends of a towel under your armpits while twirling the rope (see figure 12A). If the towel drops, one or both arms are too far out. Repeat this step until you can jump successfully without the towel.

- Keep your wrists relaxed. You will be twirling the rope with your arms and shoulders to avoid any repetitive stress to the wrist. This is very important for those that may have had a repetitive stress or other type of injury to one or both wrists.

14

- Do not lock your knees, wrists, or elbows when doing any of these exercises.

- Always look straight ahead when twirling; forcing your head up or looking down at your feet will cause discomfort and tightness in the neck and upper back. Keep your head and shoulders relaxed.

- Concentrate on slow, controlled movements. After becoming comfortable with twirling backwards, you can then increase the speed of the rope by making smaller circular movements with your arms.

- Listen to your body. Do not try to do too much too soon. Work within your limits. As long as there is a tomorrow, you'll be able to master what might seem difficult today.

- Adopt a deep rhythmic breathing pattern during your workout. Your breathing should be slow and natural. Deep breaths help you concentrate and stay relaxed.

figure 3

15

- For a complete workout, proceed through the following sequence of exercises. As you become familiar with all of the exercises presented, change their order and intensity to personalize your workout. When **IROPING** indoors, listen to your favorite music and create your own steps and moves.

- Establish a regular exercise routine. Studies continue to show it is better to do 20 - 30 minutes of exercise at least 3-4 times a week rather than 1-2 hours once a week.

The quality of a person's life is in direct proportion to their commitment to excellence, regardless of their chosen field of endeavor. —Vince Lombardi

EXERCISES:

17

Warm Up

Before you begin your jump rope sessions, take 5-10 minutes to perform warm up exercises. This can be as simple as jogging in place or light gentle stretches. Remember stretches should be slow and relaxed while you concentrate on specific muscles. To avoid injury, do not bounce or stretch to the point where you experience pain.

The following stretches are just a few basic examples you can incorporate into your workout. Keep in mind that there are different versions of these exercises and that they may vary in degree of difficulty. *Always listen to your body. Stretching should not be painful.*

Stretching Exercises:

Remember that your breathing should be slow and natural.

Neck:
- Turn your head slowly from side to side several times to help relax and warm up the neck muscles.
- Lower your chin slowly to your chest then slowly up until you are looking straight ahead.
- Repeat.
- Slowly tip your head side to side.
- Repeat several times.

Shoulders:
- Roll your shoulders forward several times and then backward several times while keeping your arms at your sides.

Shoulders and Neck:
- Sit or stand with your arms hanging loosely at your sides.
- Take a slow deep breath while shrugging your shoulders up.
- Hold position for 5 seconds.
- Slowly exhale while relaxing your shoulders downward.

Shoulders and Upper Back: (Figure 4)
- Sit or stand with fingers interlaced behind your head, elbows straight out to sides, upper body aligned.
- Pull shoulder blades together and create a feeling of tension through your upper back and shoulder blades.

figure 4

18

- Hold this position for 5 seconds and then relax.
- Repeat 1-3 times.

figure 5A

figure 5B

Triceps, Top of Shoulders, Waist: (Figure 5)

- Stand or sit with your arms overhead; your knees should be slightly flexed.
- Hold your elbow with the hand of the opposite arm.
- Pull your elbow behind your head gently as you slowly lean to your side until a mild stretch is felt.
- Hold 10 to 15 seconds.
- Repeat on other side.

Chest (Pectorals) and Inside Upper Arms: (Figure 6)

- Coil or fold jump rope or towel to about 16 inches as you would an extension cord.
- Stand and hold rope or towel behind you at both ends, hands far apart for free movement.

figure 6A

- Straighten arms up and over your head then down and behind your back.
- Hold the stretch at any place during the movement for 10 to 15 seconds; *do not force the stretch!*

Figure 6B

Hands:
- Extend your hands in front of you.
- Spread your fingers as far apart as you can (until stretching tension is felt).
- Hold position for 10 seconds, then relax.
- Repeat.

Lower Back:
- Place your hands on your hips and gently bend backwards for 10 seconds, then relax and repeat.

Lower Back, Hip and Hamstring: (Figure 7)
- Lie on the floor with your legs straight or with one leg bent.
- Gently pull your right knee to your chest.
- Hold this position between 10 - 30 seconds then relax.
- Repeat stretch for the left leg.

Figure 7

Lower Back and Groin: (Figure 8)

* Sit on the floor with the soles of your feet together holding onto your toes and feet.
* Gently and slowly pull yourself forward, bending from the hips.
* Hold this position for 10 - 30 seconds; *do not bounce!*
* Take slow deep breaths.

(alternate version)

Figure 8

* Sit on the floor with the soles of your feet together holding onto your toes or ankles, draw your heels toward your buttocks.
* Gently and slowly lean forward bending from the hips; *keep your back slightly rounded.*
* Push down gently on your legs with your elbows to stretch your knees toward the floor.

21

Inner Thigh and Groin: (Figure 9)

* Stand with your feet pointed straight ahead, and spaced a little more than shoulder width apart.
* Bend your right knee slightly and move your left hip downward toward your right knee.
* Hold this position for approximately 15 seconds.
* Repeat this stretch for the other side.

Figure 9

If you feel it necessary, hold on to a chair or rail to maintain your balance.

Hamstrings: (Figure 10)

You may use your floor markers as reference points for this stretch.

- Sit on the floor with your legs extended to form a "V".
- Gently and slowly lean forward to touch your right ankle or toes. Your back should be straight.

Figure 10A

- Slowly lift back up and return to your starting position.
- Slowly lean forward to touch the center of the "V".
- Slowly return to your starting position.

Figure 10B

- Slowly lean forward to touch your left ankle or toes.
- Return and repeat sequence.

Upper Abdominals: (Figure 11)

You may use your floor markers for this exercise.

- Sit on the floor with your hands at your sides and palms down.
- Bend your knees to 45-degree angles.
- Gently, with a slight curve to you back lean back slowly until your back touches.

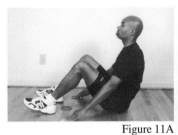

Figure 11A

- Slowly return to your starting position keeping your back slightly curved.

Figure 11B

Stationary Techniques:
Four types of Twirls / Holding the Handles

Standard Twirl:
(Figure 12)
The standard twirl allows you to condition your biceps and triceps. With the rope positioned at the front of your feet, initiate the twirl by positioning your elbows close to your waist and your forearms at about 45 degree angles from your waist. Slowly move your arms in an

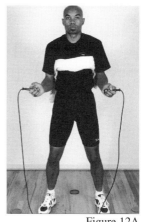

Figure 12A

upward and circular motion. You may want to try this first without the rope just to get a feel for the movement.

One way to obtain proper arm positioning is to hold the ends of a towel under your armpits while twirling the rope. If the towel drops, one or both arms are too far out. Repeat this step until you can jump successfully without the towel.

23

Figure 12B

Figure 12C

Figure 13A

Figure 13B

Figure 13C

Rowing: (Figure 13) This technique is different from the standard twirl but allows you to simulate a rowing motion while working your upper back, chest and tricep muscles. Hold the rope handles at chest height with your palms facing down and your thumbs on the ends of the handles (the rope should be toward the outside of the body as pictured). Begin the rowing motion by rotating your arms and shoulders upward in a smooth circular motion then downward toward your waist. Try this a few times without the rope and then slowly with the rope. In both cases, it might be helpful to divide the re-volution into two steps until you are able to jump through the rope successfully and with ease.

24

Notes:

25

There are two ways of exerting one's strength: one by pushing down; the other by pulling up. - Booker T. Washington

Figure 14A

Biceps curl:
(Figure 14) Hold the handles in the standard twirl position; and turn your palms upward. Keeping your wrists relaxed, begin to twirl the rope by moving your arms at the elbow in an upward circular motion almost as if you were lifting weights. Remember the speed of the rope is dependent upon the size of the circles you make with your arms. Your arm motions should be smooth, not choppy. The smaller the circles, the faster the twirl. The opposite is

Figure 14B

27

true for larger circles. Practice until you are comfortable.

Figure 14C

Extended arms:
(Figure 15) The extended arms position works the upper arm and shoulder muscles (latisimus dorsi and deltoids). Hold the handles in the standard position. As you twirl the rope, begin to extend your arms outward as far

Figure 15A

28

Figure 15B

as you can until they are almost parallel to the ground. It is important to have the proper length rope because as you extend your arms outward, the rope will become shorter. You must keep your upper body erect without shifting your weight over your knees or jumping higher off the ground.

NOTE: When twirling, remember that speed is not necessary. Do not rush these steps and concentrate on staying as low to the ground as possible, allowing the minimum amount of space between the ground and the bottom of your feet.

Basic Stationary Jumps:

The Double Foot, Alternate Foot, Staggered Feet, Lunge, Cross Step, Side-to-Side, Ins and Outs, Modified Jumping Jacks/Scissors, Running in Place.

Double Foot:

(Figure 16) The double foot position is perhaps one of the most basic and most common of jump rope steps. This step conditions the upper thigh and calve muscles.

Figure 16

Begin with both feet together, flex your knees slightly and push off the ground with your toes, and land lightly on the balls of your feet. Both feet should leave the ground and land together. A variation of this step is to spread your feet apart about shoulder distance and repeat the jumping/landing stages.

Alternate Foot:

(Figure 17) This step, commonly referred to as the "skipping" technique, is done by alternating the feet up and down while twirling the rope. Remember to land on the balls of the feet.

Figure 17

NOTE: Start slowly and *gradually* increase the speed of the rope.

Staggered: (Figure 18) Begin this step by placing one foot slightly in front of the other. Flex your knees and push off the ground and land lightly on the balls of the feet. Try doing this 5 - 10 times then switch feet. Keep your head up, shoulders relaxed, and back straight.

Figure 18

Lunge: (Figure 19) The lunge is a modification of the staggered foot position. Begin as you would the staggered jump; however, alternate your feet with every revolution. This may require some practice. Be patient and take your time. When you become more comfortable with this movement, increase the distance between your feet. This movement is excellent for working the quadriceps, calves and gluteal muscles.

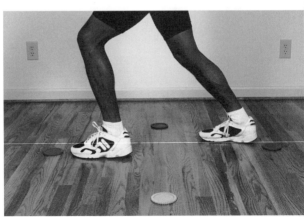

Figure 19

Alternate Leg Lifts:
(Figure 20) The alternate leg lifts technique works the quadriceps and helps improve balance while roping. When performed properly, this technique should look as if you are marching in place. Begin with the double foot bounce and

Figure 20A

Figure 20B

gradually move into a stationary march. For beginners, try not to lift your legs too high. Start off with low lifts and gradually begin to lift higher as you become comfortable with the steps.

31

Cross step:
(Figure 21) You might want to begin this step by practicing without the rope. Start with both feet together, bend your knees and push off with your toes. Again, look straight ahead, keep your shoulders relaxed and your back straight. When you are off the

Figure 21

ground, cross your lower legs and land with your legs crossed. After repeated practice you should be able to make consecutive jumps alternating left leg and right leg crosses. This is an excellent drill for improving foot speed and vertical jumping.

TIP: You can also start this technique with your feet crossed.

Figure 22A

Side-to-Side:
(Figure 22) Before you begin this step, it might be helpful to place three pieces of tape on the ground approximately 12 inches from each other (one center strip and one strip on the right and left of the center strip). These strips of tape will serve as landing markers. Once the tape has been placed on the floor, stand on the center strip with both feet close to each other. Bend your knees, push off with your toes and try to land on either the right or left marker and then back to the center. Both feet should leave and land together. The floor markers included in the IROPE Optimum Performance Achievement

Figure 22B

Kit can be used in place of the pieces of tape. Instead of landing on the floor markers, simply move your feet in the direction of the marker(s).

Figure 23A

33

Figure 23B

Left and Right Ins and Outs:

(Figure 23) For this exercise you will need the three landing markers used in the Side-to-Side technique. Begin by standing on the center marker using the double foot jump. Make three double foot jumps and, on the fourth jump, move either the left or right leg toward the appropriate marker. You should be able to touch the marker with your toes as you land. Alternate from left to right and so on.

Jumping Jacks/ Scissors:

(Figure 24) Begin with both feet together. Bend your knees slightly, push off of the ground with your toes, and land lightly on the balls of your feet. Push off again and land with your feet spread apart about shoulder width. Push off a third time

Figure 24A

and land with your feet together. Alternate this landing sequence with your feet together and apart.

34

Figure 24B

Running in Place:

(Figure 25) This technique involves running in place as you jump through the rope. In order to become comfortable with a pace or rhythm, start without the rope. Run in place while going through the standard, rowing and biceps curls twirling motions. Many have found using the rowing motion makes this

Figure 25

exercise a little easier. Once you've established a comfortable rhythm, pick up the rope and begin running in place. Start off with a slow but comfortable pace; and as you become more proficient you can increase your pace.

Basic Mobile Techniques:

To enhance your workout, try adding directional movement to the stationary techniques from the preceding pages. This is simply done by either taking a small step forward or backward, or to the right or left, before returning to your base marker (center strip). As you become more comfortable with these movements, add more steps in either direction. Continue doing so until you are able to move in several different directions without having to stop twirling. Again, it is always helpful to try these movements first without the rope, and then with it. The more common movements that should be practiced are the staggered feet, slides, lunge, ins/outs, and running. These movements form the foundation for all mobile techniques.

Slides:

(Figure 26) Slides are the mobile form of the "ins/outs" technique. Slides are accomplished by moving to the right or left several steps then back in the opposite direction toward your starting point (Refer to fi-

Figure 26A

Figure 26B

gure 23). This technique, which is a little advanced, is an excellent exercise to improve hand-eye-foot coordination, speed and agility. As with all the exercises, start with slow controlled movements and gradually increase your speed.

To add a little variety to this technique, try working out with a partner. Your partner can act as a guide or leader and does not need a rope. Facing each other, you will follow your partners lead and move accordingly. This technique is not only challenging but can be a lot of fun.

The slides technique is an excellent technique to master if you enjoy tennis, basketball, football and soccer where a good portion of your movements are determined by reacting to or anticipating your opponents moves.

Marching: (Refer to figure 20, alternate leg lifts) The marching technique is the mobile form of the alternate leg lifts. Follow the instructions for alternate leg lifts and begin to take a few steps forward.

Rope Walking:
(Figure 27) Perhaps the most expressive and unique movement when it comes to jump roping is rope walking. This movement is unique to the Innovative Roping concepts in that it is the embodiment of the low impact, total body conditioning philosophy of ***IROPING.***

(Photograph by Donna Calcote)

Figure 27A

37

To begin the walk, start in the double foot position; then move into a stationary lunge. Do a few lunges in place then begin to move forward. Initially, try landing on the balls of the feet. Eventually try the more natural way of walking by landing on the heel first, and then rolling your foot forward toward the ball of your foot and pushing off with the toes. Once you have built up your confidence, enhance your walk-

(Photograph by Samuel Coffman)

ing routine by lengthening your stride and picking up the pace. At first this may seem a little awkward, but don't worry; the more you practice the smoother you'll become. Keep your head up, back straight, breathe deeply and stay relaxed.

There is more to life than increasing
speed.
– Mohandas K. Ghandi

Q: When can I expect to feel like I know what I am doing?

A: *Only time and consistent exercise sessions will determine how soon you will begin to feel like you know what you're doing. As with learning anything new, practice, practice, practice. Don't lose focus and stay calm and relaxed. At anytime, don't hesitate to go back to some of the steps you can perform with ease to rebuild your confidence, then proceed to a more complex or challenging step.*

Do not become discouraged if the rope misses. This will happen even at the most advanced levels. Take a break and determine what is causing you to miss. Sometimes improper arm positioning may shorten or lengthen the rope which may cause you to miss. Break up your sets by trying different techniques. Be mindful of the surface you are jumping on; avoid gravelly surfaces and tall grassy areas. Should you experience any unusual pains or discomfort during these drills stop at once.

39

Q: How can I build my endurance and prevent my upper body from getting tired while practicing drills and rope walking?

A: *The best way to build your endurance and to prevent upper body fatigue is to alternate between the different twirling techniques mentioned earlier. Whether you're practicing stationary or mobile drills or you're rope walking, alternating twirling techniques keeps the upper body relaxed and will help improve your endurance.*

Q: How do I keep my lower body relaxed when jumping?

A: *The basic principle of alternating steps during your workout not only allows you to work different muscle groups; but it also relaxes those lower body muscle groups that might get over worked when you focus too much on one step or technique.*

Don't wait until you begin feeling fatigued to switch to another technique.

MEASURING YOUR

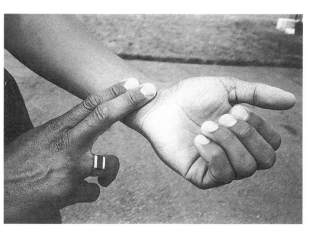

HEART RATE:

If you are middle aged or older or have a preexisting health condition, please consult your physician for advice on measuring your heart rate and setting your heart rate zone before beginning this exercise program. The following calculations are not meant to replace the advice of your doctor.

As a rule, it is always wise to monitor the intensity of your workout. Your heart rate zone is perhaps the best gauge for that. This measurement can give you an indication as to whether you are working too hard or not hard enough.

To calculate your maximum heart rate, subtract your age from 220 beats/minute. To achieve cardiovascular benefit from your workout, you should exercise between 60% to 80% of your heart rate. For example, if you are 36 years old you would subtract 36 from 220 beats per minute and get 184. Sixty percent of 184 is 110 beats/minute. Eighty percent is 147 beats/minute (this figure represents the fastest your heart should beat at your age). Therefore, your heart rate zone is 110 - 147.

After five minutes of exercise, determine your heart rate by taking your pulse for 10 seconds and multiply by 6, or for 15 seconds and multiply by four. If this figure is below your 60% figure you may want to increase the intensity of your workout. On the other hand, if it is too high, slow down or stop. When you first begin your exercise program it is also good to take your resting heart rate when you first wake up. This reading is important in establishing a baseline record.

As part of charting your progress, include your average weekly heart rate on the progress chart on pages 43 and 45.

Example for a 36-year-old:

$$220 - 36 = 184 \times .60 = 110.4$$
$$220 - 36 = 184 \times .80 = 147.2$$

Target Heart Rate Zone: 110 - 147

For Your Record:

220 - _____ = _____ x   .60 *   = _____

　　　your age　max. heart　　　　　　　　current
　　　　　　　　　rate　　　　　　　　　　　level of
　　　　　　　　　　　　　　　　　　　　　fitness

*May be substituted with .70 for intermediates or .80 for advanced.

Jumping Rope the Second Time Around

Use the following grid to chart your heart rate.

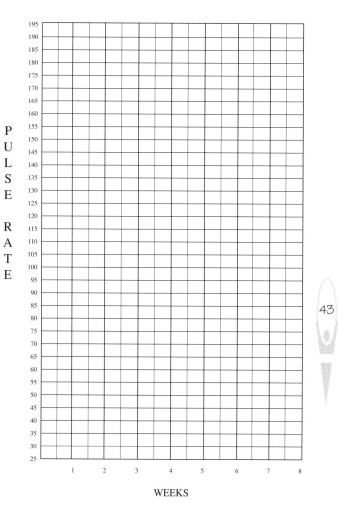

P
U
L
S
E

R
A
T
E

195
190
185
180
175
170
165
160
155
150
145
140
135
130
125
120
115
110
105
100
95
90
85
80
75
70
65
60
55
50
45
40
35
30
25

1   2   3   4   5   6   7   8

WEEKS

43

The Chinese Bamboo

In the far east the people plant a tree called the Chinese Bamboo. During the first four years they water and fertilize the plant with seemingly little or no results. Then the fifth year they again apply water and fertilizer - - and in five weeks time the tree grows ninety feet! The obvious question is: Did it grow ninety feet in five weeks, or did it grow ninety feet in five years? The answer is it grew ninety feet in five years. Because if at any time the people had stopped watering and fertilizing the tree it would have died.

44

Many times our dreams and plans appear not to be succeeding. We are tempted to give up and quit trying. Instead, we need to continue to water and fertilize those dreams and plans, nurturing the seeds of the vision God has placed within us. Because we know that if we do not quit, if we display perseverance and endurance, we will also reap a bountiful harvest.

— source unknown.

Jumping Rope the Second Time Around

Use the following grid to chart your heart rate.

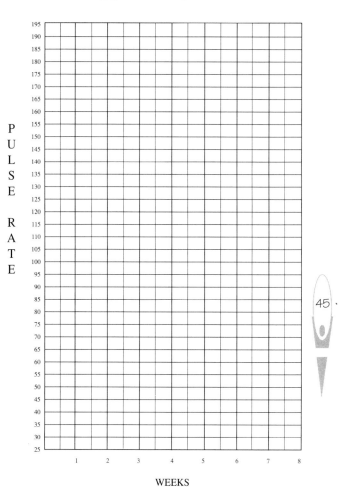

PULSE RATE

WEEKS

Carlos Coffman

MY COMMITMENT

In all eternity there will be only one me. Now is my time to SHINE! *The Daily Word*

Today I, _____, commit myself to the following goals and activities for the improvement of my health for me, my family, and my loved ones. This agreement with myself shall be effective from this _____ day of _____ (month/year) and beyond the attainment of these goals.

The goals that I have set for myself are: (ex. eating well balanced and healthier meals, becoming more physically active through regular exercise, encourage others to live a healthier life, etc.)

_____

_____

To pursue these goals, I am committed to perform the following activities on a regular basis at least _____ days a week. (IROPE, walk, swim, bicycle, gardening, etc.) I have set aside at least 30 minutes for each day I have committed to exercise.

I have identified at least three people (family members, co-workers, friends, etc.) who understand my goals and who will help me remain focused and stick to my program objectives. They are: 1. _____

2. _____

3. _____

The benefits which I will realize by fulfilling my goals are:

_____

_____

The benefits others will realize by me fulfilling my goals are:

_____

_____

_____   _____
Signature   Date

_____   _____
Witness   Date

47

If initiative is the ability to do the right thing, then efficiency is the ability to do the thing right.

— Kelly Miller

48

MY COMMITMENT

In all eternity there will be only one me. Now is my time to SHINE! *The Daily Word*

Today I, _____, commit myself to the following goals and activities for the improvement of my health for me, my family, and my loved ones. This agreement with myself shall be effective from this _____ day of _____ (month/year) and beyond the attainment of these goals.

The goals that I have set for myself are: (ex. eating well balanced and healthier meals, becoming more physically active through regular exercise, encourage others to live a healthier life, etc.)

_____

_____

To pursue these goals, I am committed to perform the following activities on a regular basis at least _____ days a week. (IROPE, walk, swim, bicycle, gardening, etc.) I have set aside at least 30 minutes for each day I have committed to exercise.

49

I have identified at least three people (family members, co-workers, friends, etc.) who understand my goals and who will help me remain focused and stick to my program objectives. They are: 1. _____

2. _____

3. _____

The benefits which I will realize by fulfilling my goals are:

_____

_____

The benefits others will realize by me fulfilling my goals are:

_____

_____

_____   _____
Signature   Date

_____   _____
Witness   Date

Carlos Coffman

WORKING TOWARD YOUR GOALS

Whatever IROPE activities you choose, setting clear goals will help you achieve the results you want. In order to maximize the benefits of this program start off by setting realistic goals that are not too easily reached nor too difficult to accomplish.

The chart on page 53 is provided to assist you with setting your goals. As you progress, feel free to personalize your workout by adding steps you may have created, and TAKE CREDIT FOR YOUR SUCCESSES. Vary your upper body workout by using the different twirling motions (standard, biceps, rowing and extended arms) discussed in the preceding sections. Remember to always practice proper form, stay relaxed, land lightly on the balls of the feet during drills, and strike the ground lightly with the heel when rope walking. Remain patient and practice rhythmic breathing patterns. Feel free to take breaks between sets.

51

	BEGINNER	INTERMEDIATE	ADVANCED
WARM-UP / COOL DOWN stretches walking jogging in place without the rope	approx. 5 - 10 min.	approx. 5 - 10 min.	approx. 5 - 10 min.
STAGGERED 1 set =5 jumps 5 jumps with right foot forward then backward TIP: switch to left foot forward	2 sets	5 sets	15 sets
LUNGES 1 set = 5 steps in one direction (5 steps forward is equivalent to one set) TIP: practice moving in both directions	3 sets	10 sets	15 sets
SLIDES 1 set = 5 steps in both directions (5 steps to the right, then 5 steps to the left is equivalent to one set)	3 sets	10 sets	15 sets
ROPE WALKING Begin by rope walking 30 feet (approx. 10 steps) and increase distance to 100 yards until you can complete ¼ mile. TIP: practice on a marked track; usually one lap is about ¼ mile	¼ mile in 7 min. ½ mile in 14 min. 1 mile in 26 min.	¼ mile in 5 min. ½ mile in 10 min. 1 mile in 20 min.	¼ mile in 4 min. ½ mile in 8 min. 1 mile in 16 min.

52

How did I feel before exercising? _____

How did I feel while exercising? _____

How did I feel after exercising? _____

What obstacles did I overcome or encounter? _____

_____

What will I do differently tomorrow? _____

_____

PROGRESS CHART

Week/Date	Warm-up Activity	Technique Lunge, Ins/Outs, etc…	Number of Sets	Distance Rope Walking 1/4m, 1/2m, 1mile or more	Cool Down Activity	Length of workout in minutes	Heart rate

Carlos Coffman

Notes:

54

How did I feel before exercising? _____

How did I feel while exercising? _____

How did I feel after exercising? _____

What obstacles did I overcome or encounter? _____

_____

What will I do differently tomorrow? _____

_____

PROGRESS CHART

Week/Date	Warm-up Activity	Technique Lunge, Ins/Outs, etc....	Number of Sets	Distance Rope Walking 1/4m, 1/2m, 1mile or more	Cool Down Activity	Length of workout in minutes	Heart rate

55

Carlos Coffman

Notes:

STRESS RELIEVERS: Tips For Managing Stress

The following tips may be used to help reduce and manage stress:

IN EVERYDAY LIFE

1. Eat balanced meals.
2. Eliminate or avoid excessive use of caffeine, cigarettes, and alcohol.
3. Drink plenty of water every day.
4. Exercise regularly at least 30 minutes per day three times a week.
5. Keep a positive mental attitude.
6. Get enough rest.
7. Take up an activity you enjoy outside of work.
8. Read something inspirational every day.

57

IN THE WORKPLACE

1. Take a brisk walk at lunchtime.
2. Work at better communication with people.
3. Take short breaks and alter your work activities.
4. Listen to relaxing music.
5. Take one minute stretch breaks daily.

The happiness of your life depends on the quality of your thoughts.
-Anonymous

Notes:

_____

_____

_____

_____

_____

_____

_____

_____

_____

_____

_____

_____

_____

_____

_____

_____

_____

_____

_____

_____

_____

_____

_____

_____

_____

_____

_____

_____

_____

_____

_____

_____

_____

IROPE TRAVEL TIPS

1. Begin planning your workout before leaving home; call the hotel where you will be staying and ask if it has a fitness center or has visiting privileges for its guests at a nearby health club.

2. Don't forget to pack your jump rope along with the appropriate workout clothing and shoes. If you plan to workout in the early morning hours or after the sun sets, pack reflective clothing and a safety light that clips onto your clothing or can be worn around your upper arm.

3. When you arrive at your destination, become familiar with the area where you are staying. Take a short drive or walk to map your course. Note the level of pedestrian and vehicular traffic. Make sure the area is a safe place to exercise. Don't take unnecessary risks.

4. Use the Internet to identify running clubs in the area where you will be staying. Most running clubs have web sites that contain a wealth of information about the best and safest places to workout, as well as valuable tips on the area itself.

5. Identify any nearby parks, paved jogging trails or high school or college tracks where you can safely rope walk. I've always enjoyed early morning rope walks through Piedmont Park in Atlanta, Georgia, along Chicago's Lake Shore Drive, Los Angeles' Venice Beach, Austin, Texas' Town Lake and the O'Dell Weeks fitness trail in Aiken, South Carolina. Most major cities and even some small towns have popular spots where both residents and visitors run, walk, and jog.

6. If you are not comfortable venturing away from the hotel, you can always jump rope in the hotel parking lot (weather permitting). Find two adjacent parking spaces and practice some of the roping techniques discussed earlier. I always find it helpful to utilize the line dividing the two spaces as a reference point for lunges, scissors, side-to-sides, etc. This is a great opportunity to become creative and come up with new steps.

59

7. Rope walk a few laps around the hotel parking lot. Time yourself and try making each lap faster than the previous. (PLEASE WATCH FOR TRAFFIC).

8. Use the stairs not only as a means of getting to or leaving your room, but also incorporate a few flights into your daily workout before or after your IROPE sessions. Make sure that the stair wells are safe, well lit and regularly used.

9. If an outdoor workout is not possible determine the best and safest place to exercise. Remember you can always jump rope in your room. As long as you land lightly on the balls of your feet and are using the **IROPE** techniques properly, you will not disturb other guests in adjacent rooms.

10. Take advantage of the exercise facilities on hand if available.

11. Always perform warmup and cool down stretches before and after your workout.

12. Eat properly and try to maintain your water intake as if you were at home.

13. HAVE FUN!

Notes:

_____

_____

_____

_____

_____

_____

_____

_____

_____

_____

_____

_____

_____

_____

61

_____

_____

_____

_____

_____

_____

_____

_____

_____

_____

_____

_____

_____

_____

_____

USING YOUR OPTIMUM PERFORMANCE ACHIEVEMENT KIT

Use the IROPE Optimum Performance Achievement Kit to enhance your personal or group jump rope program. Each kit includes: *Jumping Rope the Second Time Around*, an adjustable jump rope, 4 floor markers, a workout chart and a mesh carrying bag.

Now that you've become familiar with the IROPE techniques described in the preceding sections, use the four floor markers as reference points in place of the strips of tape mentioned earlier. Start by mentally drawing an imaginary six-foot circle on the jumping surface. Stand in the center of the circle and place the first marker three feet directly in front of you. Turn completely around and facing the opposite direction place a second marker three feet in front of you. Turning to and facing your left, place the third marker three feet in front of you and lastly, face the opposite direction again and place the remaining marker three feet in front of you. A center marker is not needed because you will not touch the markers with your feet when executing the drills.

Once you have set up your workout area, or "playing field", begin your workout without the jump rope by using the markers to go through the techniques you plan to practice. Slowly practice different techniques with varying degrees of difficulty. Try to include techniques that work different upper and lower body muscle groups. This step can serve as your warm up as well as your cool down before and after your IROPE sessions.

After you have completed a few sets of stationary techniques, rearrange the floor markers farther apart in a straight line with about 4 to 5 feet between each marker. Start about 3 feet behind the first marker. Begin with the stationary double foot jump then proceed to the slide technique in the direction of the fourth marker. Try to make it to the fourth marker without stopping then begin to move back to your starting point. Do a few sets of this technique then move to more difficult techniques that include moving in between and back and forth of the markers. As you get better, add more markers to create different and more challenging courses. Don't be afraid to be creative. Whether working out alone, with a partner, or a group try to complete these drills in less time as you move through the "obstacle" course.

TIP #1:Record your sessions on the workout chart. (The second chart is perforated for easy removal)

TIP #2:Take your kit with you on vacation or on business trips.

TIP #3:Keep a set of floor markers at the office and use them when you take a 1-minute fitness break.

OPTIMUM PERFORMANCE ACHIEVEMENT KIT
WORKOUT & PROGRESS CHART

DAY TIME START END	STD. TWIRL NO. REPS	ROW NO. REPS	BICEPS CURL NO. REPS	EXTD. ARMS NO. REPS	LEFT CROSS NO. REPS	RIGHT CROSS NO. REPS	HOLD CROSS NO. REPS	TOTAL JUMPS
DBL FT	10	10	10	5	5	5	10	55
ALT. FT	10	10	10	5	5	5	10	55
TOTAL	20	20	20	10	10	10	20	110
DBL FOOT								
ALT. FOOT								
STAG.								
LUNGE INS/ OUT								
JUMPING JACKS								
SLIDES								
LEG LIFTS								
TOTAL								

65

Champions aren't made in gyms. Champions are made from something they have deep inside them - a desire, a dream, a vision. They have to have last-minute stamina, they have to be a little faster, they have to have the skill, and the will. But the will must be stronger than the skill. —Muhammad Ali

OPTIMUM PERFORMANCE ACHIEVEMENT KIT
WORKOUT & PROGRESS CHART

DAY TIME START END	STD. TWIRL NO. REPS	ROW NO. REPS	BICEPS CURL NO. REPS	EXTD. ARMS NO. REPS	LEFT CROSS NO. REPS	RIGHT CROSS NO. REPS	HOLD CROSS NO. REPS	TOTAL JUMPS
DBL FT	10	10	10	5	5	5	10	55
ALT. FT	10	10	10	5	5	5	10	55
TOTAL	20	20	20	10	10	10	20	110
DBL FOOT								
ALT. FOOT								
STAG.								
LUNGE INS/ OUT								
JUMPING JACKS								
SLIDES								
LEG LIFTS								
TOTAL								

67

About the Author

Carlos Coffman started jump roping at the age of 27 after injuring his knee during a routine mid distance run. At the suggestion of a friend he adopted and perfected the backward twirling and multi-directional movement techniques. What initially began as a personal challenge to overcome an injury and remain fit, gave way to the modernization of traditional jump roping into a total body conditioning program. Innovative Roping combines an old, familiar childhood "toy" with a modern day approach to physical fitness that can be enjoyed by just about anyone, anywhere, at anytime.

Mr. Coffman has "rope walked" several marathons including the Marine Corps (Washington, DC), LaSalle-Banks/Chicago (Chicago, IL.), Motorola (Austin, TX.) and the City of Los Angeles Marathons (Los Angeles, CA) as well as countless half-marathons, ten-milers and 10-Ks throughout the country. In addition, he has demonstrated his unique style of "roping" on local cable shows and at several fitness expos in the metropolitan Washington, D.C. area.

Mr. Coffman works in the field of Occupational Safety and Health. He believes a safe and healthy work force builds healthy organizations that in turn can contribute to strengthening our families and rebuilding our communities, nation and world.

69

IROPE develops and leads workshops and classes for churches, schools, businesses and special needs groups.

Let **IROPE** assist you in achieving your fitness goals with an old fashioned "childhood toy" destined to bring back memories of fun and laughter.

For more information on Innovative Roping and **IROPE** products and services, please visit our website at www.irope.com or email us at irope@prodigy.net

Our mailing address is:

Innovative Roping, Inc.
P.O. Box 2136
Bowie, Maryland 20718

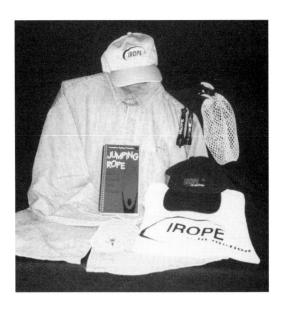

Carlos Coffman

It's been said...

"Whether you're bored with your workout routine and want a new challenge or you're trying to regai fitness after a running or knee injury, this bool will have something to offer. I highly recommenc it."- Don "Doc" Mann (retired US Navy Seal) - Army Times

"Coffman's method of jump roping can be a more efficient way of using your energy, and a more ef ficient way to condition your body than some of the workouts you're used to. It's safe for most peopl over 25, it costs less than an AB slide and it can L done almost anywhere."- Patricia Cinelli, ACE cer tified personal trainer

"It's easy to learn and it's fun to do because you'r able to move in different directions instead of jump ing in a stationary position."- Jean-Keith Fagan, Publisher - Capital Community News

"Fun, invigorating, "legs to die for" that's wha IROPE has done for me. I thought because I a "over forty and holding," that I would not and coul not learn to jump rope all over again. But Coffman detailed and inspirational approach and technique made it easy. I saw results in two weeks. No "IROPE!"" - B. Richburg

"This is a great book for those who are looking fo an alternative exercise program. As a former sea entary graduate student, I started jumping rope to lose weight. Sixty-five pounds lighter, I'm f. and trim and using Coffman's jump roping techniques to maintain my weight loss. I highly recommend this book!"- R.Y. Jackson

" The IROPE workout is simply awesome!"
-A working parent

"Finding time to workout has always been my chal lenge, but this technique takes less time and it's fun." - Miranda